GOOD NIGHT, HUMAN

written and illustrated by

C. MAALF

Good night, Gentle Human,
Hush the voice in your head,
Release yourself from this world,
It's time for bed.

Remove all those clothes,
Your armour of thread,
Your daytime disguise,
It's time for bed.

Lay down your defences,
And soon you'll discover,
It's not danger that comes,
But a peace like no other.

At ease, Tiny Soldier,
To yourself just be kind,
It's time to stop fighting,
Imaginary wars in your mind.

Release the burden,
Of this part that you play,
Don't prepare for tomorrow,
By worrying today.

It's time to be small,
Yes, insignificant too,
Only then can you find me,
And know I am you.

Into your pillow,
Your head softly sinking,
I am the grace that's within you,
When you finally stop thinking.

I am that part of you,
Untethered, divine,
Eternally transcending,
All space and time.

Beckoned or not,
In your shadow I lie,
I am the voice that answers,
When you ask, who am I?

That's me right there!
Who jumped at those words,
Whose voice you just felt,
Though it can't be heard.

Who orders your heart to beat?
And your blood to flow?
How do 37 trillion cells,
Know where to go?

I am the part of you,
That animates the flesh,
That unites you to greatness,
In this cosmic mesh.

I am the music,
And you are the horn,
I'm the mighty oak,
Inside your acorn.

I connect you to that,
Which can't be explained,
The greatest I AM,
That needs not a name.

As the sunbeam is sun,
As the branch still is tree,
You thought you were the droplet,
But you are the sea.

So stop measuring your worth,
In increments so fleeting,
Like dollars or age,
Or the calories you're eating.

You're already whole,
The sum. The amount.
Slow down, stop counting,
And you'll find out what counts.

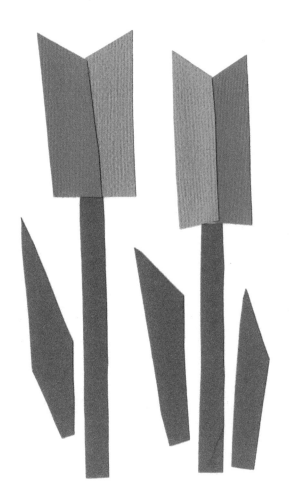

Separate the illusion,
From all that is true,
Know again the stranger,
Who was once you.

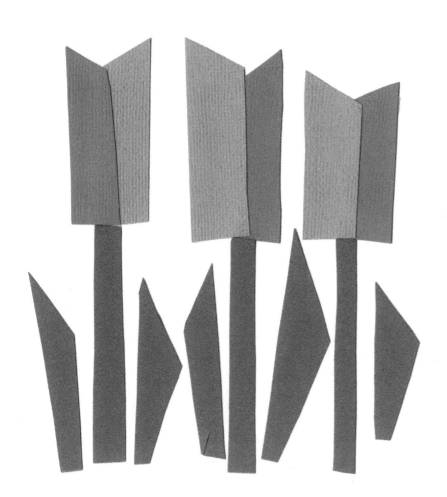

Fear not, Little Earthling,
I know all too well,
That sometimes to find me,
You must go through hell.

I see you, Human,
The struggle, the strife,
And I come to you often,
Disguised as your life.

What if everything,
Is exactly as planned?
What if all your tomorrows,
Are in my command?

So worry not, Brave Human,
Lay down your arms,
Feel the safety of knowing,
Nothing real can be harmed.

That's the secret of life,
I want you to know,
That you can conquer all,
When you let go.

Listen, My Human,
There is naught to be done,
By accepting what is,
Real change will come.

Take time to rejoice,
I'll tell you how,
Just remember two things:
You are here. It is now.

One more thing to know,
If nothing else you've heard,
Is that by finding your own light,
You find the light of the world.

Good night, Gentle Human,
I've turned out the light,
Be small and be still,
And you'll feel my might.

Pull me in with your breath,
Feel yourself unwind,
What sleep is to the body,
I am to your mind.

Tomorrow will offer,
A new light to see,
A new day of becoming,
Who you came here to be.

Sleep tight, Gentle Human,
I await you with glee,
I am the balm and the remedy,
That sets you free.

The End.
(Also known as The Beginning).

CPSIA information can be obtained
at www.ICGtesting.com
Printed in the USA
BVHW021843290422
635757BV00004B/16